Julie Lewis 778943 £6-15

C000001193

Showtunes
for Keyboard
Volume 2

As Long As He Needs Me	Oliver!	2
Believe In Yourself	The Wiz	4
Button Up Your Overcoat	Good News!	6
Charlie Girl	Charlie Girl	8
Come Follow The Band	Barnum	10
Day By Day	Godspell	12
Get Me To The Church On Time	My Fair Lady	14
Getting To Know You	The King And I	16
Give My Regards To Broadway	George M!	18
Hello Dolly!	Hello Dolly!	20
Hey There	The Pajama Game	22
Hopelessly Devoted To You	Grease	24
I Can't Get Started	Ziegfield Follies – 1936	26
June Is Bustin' Out All Over	Carousel	28
K-ra-zy For You	Crazy For You	30
Married	Cabaret	32
Maybe	Annie	34
One	A Chorus Line	36
'S Wonderful	Funny Face	38
Somewhere	West Side Story	40
Willkommen	Cabaret	42
Wouldn't It Be Loverly	My Fair Lady	44
Young Girl	Return To The Forbidden Planet	46

Music arranged and processed by Barnes Music Engraving Ltd
East Sussex TN22 4HA, UK

Cover design by xheight Limited

Published 1995

As Long As He Needs Me

Words and Music by Lionel Bart

Suggested Registration: Electric Piano
Rhythm: Soft Rock / Ballad
Tempo: ♩ = 76

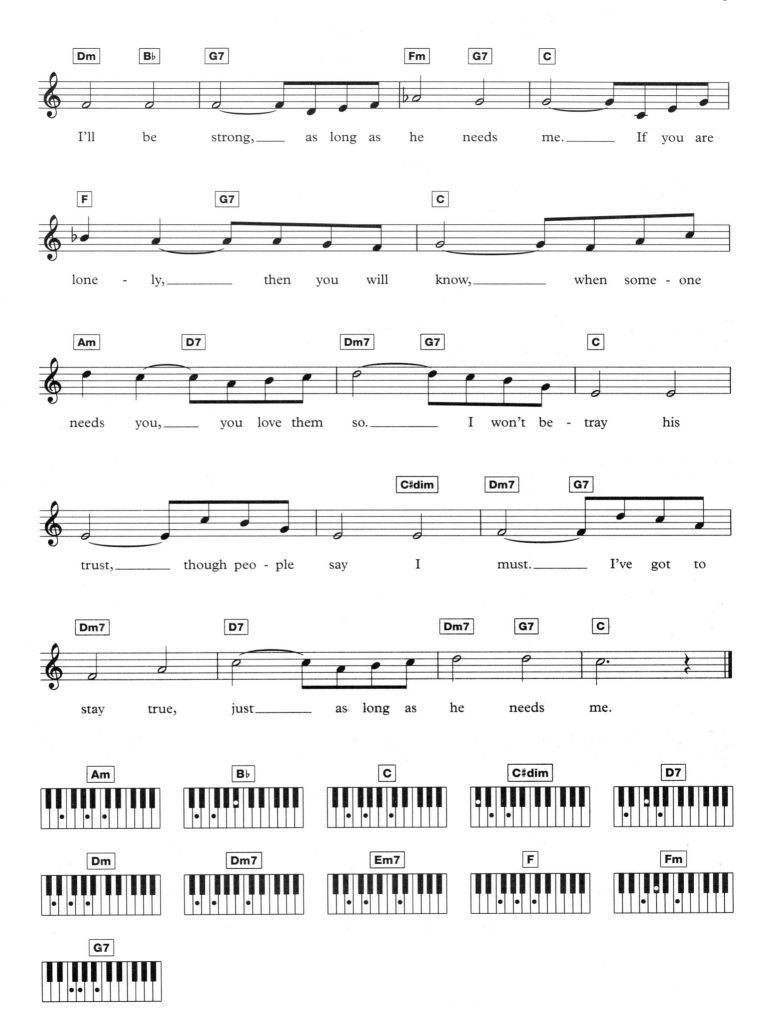

Believe In Yourself

Words and Music by Charlie Smalls

Suggested Registration: Strings
Rhythm: Soft Rock
Tempo: ♩ = 94

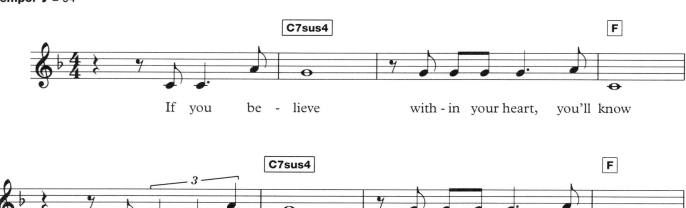

If you be - lieve with - in your heart, you'll know

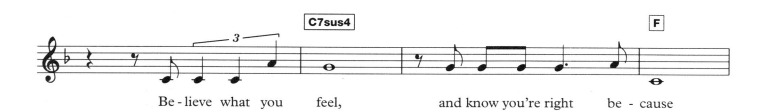

that no one can change the path that you must go.

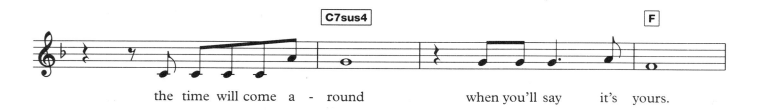

Be - lieve what you feel, and know you're right be - cause

the time will come a - round when you'll say it's yours.

Be - lieve there's a rea-son to be, be - lieve you can make time stand

still, and know from the mo-ment you try, if you be - lieve_____

Button Up Your Overcoat

Words and Music by B G DeSylva, Lew Brown and Ray Henderson

Suggested Registration: Vibraphone
Rhythm: Swing
Tempo: ♩ = 138

But-ton up your o - ver - coat___ when the wind is free,

take good care of your - self,___ you be - long to me.___

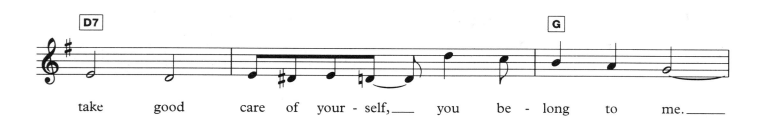

Eat an ap - ple ev - ery day,___ get to bed by three,

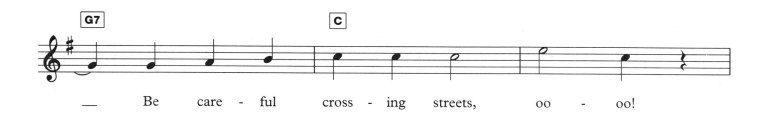

take good care of your - self,___ you be - long to me.___

___ Be care - ful cross - ing streets, oo - oo!

Don't eat meats, oo - oo! Cut out sweets,

oo - oo! You'll get a pain and ru - in your tum - tum.

Keep a - way from boot - leg hootch when you're on a spree,

take good care of your - self,___ you be - long to me.

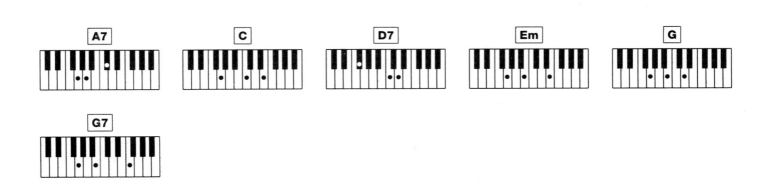

Charlie Girl

Words and Music by David Heneker and John Taylor

Suggested Registration: Clarinet
Rhythm: Swing
Tempo: ♩ = 128

You, you're great and won - der - ful, Char - lie Girl it's

you. I've gone a bun - dle on Char - lie Girl.

I'm a tongue - tied awk - ward kind_ of a fel - la_____ who

falls in love with some - one smash - ing, and then can't tell her!

Just one look at you,_ and I do my nut. I've

got a lot to say,___ but my mouth stays shut.

Though you scare me half to death, here we go then, take a breath.

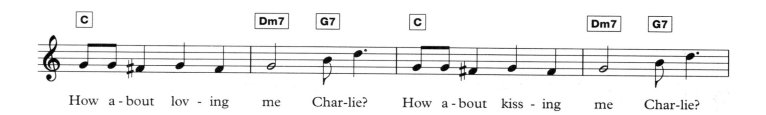

How a-bout lov-ing me Char-lie? How a-bout kiss-ing me Char-lie?

How a-bout mar-ry-ing me Char - lie Girl?_____

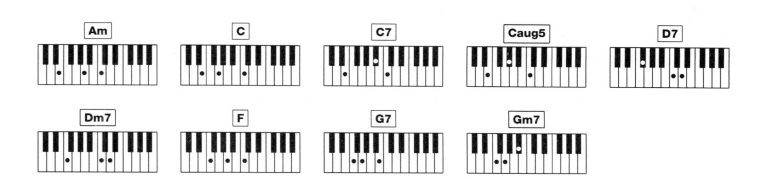

Come Follow The Band

Words by Michael Stewart / Music by Cy Coleman

Suggested Registration: Trumpet
Rhythm: Dixie / Swing
Tempo: ♩ = 154

Come fol - low the band___ where ev - er it's at,___

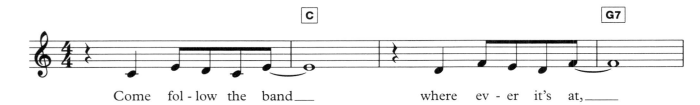

let both of your feet___ beat time to the drum, and feel your

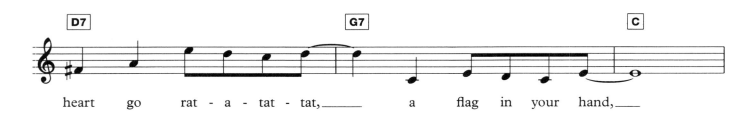

heart go rat - a - tat - tat,___ a flag in your hand,___

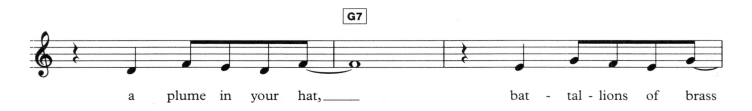

a plume in your hat,___ bat - tal - lions of brass

___ pass and catch the light.___ Is there a sight that's sweet - er than that?

___ See the pret - ty la - dy toss that ba - ton high. Ain't she cute as a

Day By Day

Words and Music by Stephen Schwartz

Suggested Registration: Flute
Rhythm: Rock / 8 Beat
Tempo: ♩ = 132

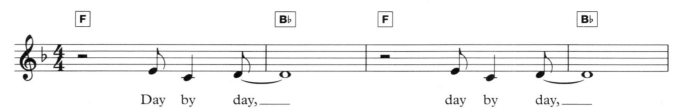

Day by day,_____ day by day,_____

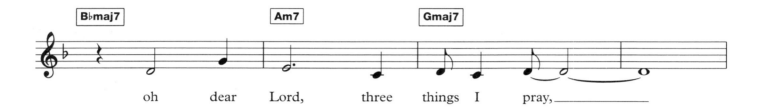

oh dear Lord, three things I pray,_____

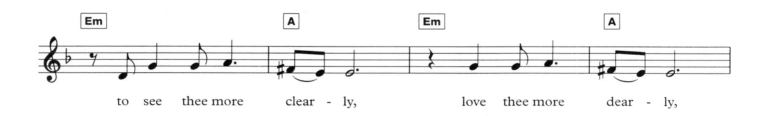

to see thee more clear - ly, love thee more dear - ly,

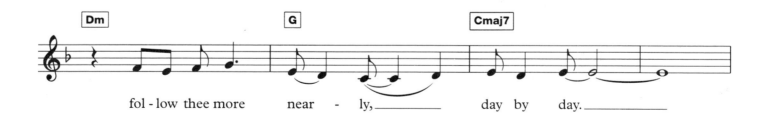

fol - low thee more near - ly,_____ day by day._____

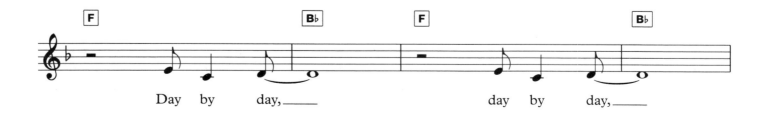

Day by day,_____ day by day,_____

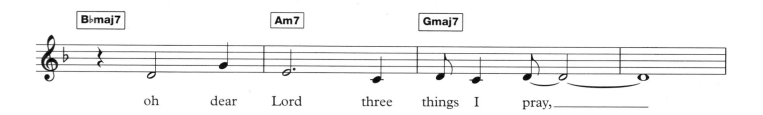

oh   dear   Lord   three   things   I   pray,_____

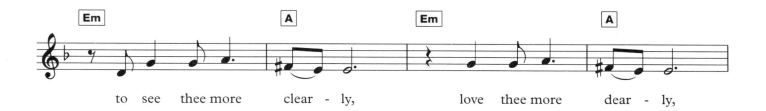

to   see   thee more   clear - ly,   love thee more   dear - ly,

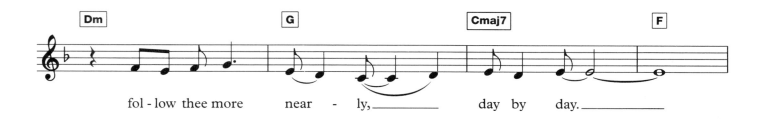

fol - low thee more   near - ly,_____   day by   day._____

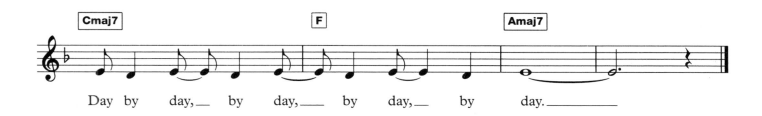

Day by   day,__ by   day,___ by   day,__ by   day._____

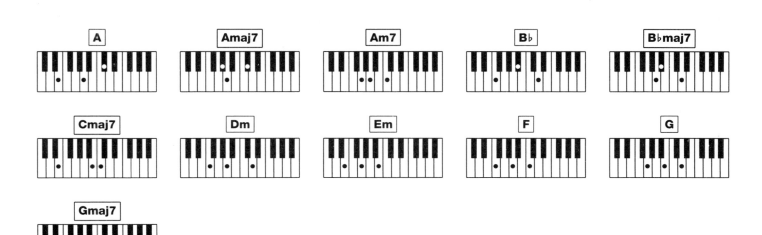

Get Me To The Church On Time

Words by Alan Jay Lerner / Music by Frederick Loewe

Suggested Registration: Trombone
Rhythm: March
Tempo: ♩ = 116

I'm get - ting mar - ried in the morn - ing.

Ding! Dong! The bells are gon - na chime.

Pull out the stop - per, let's have a whop - per, but

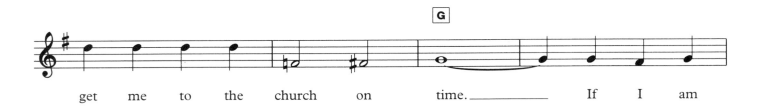

get me to the church on time. If I am

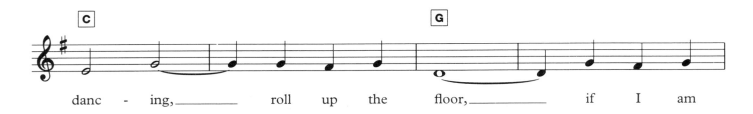

danc - ing, roll up the floor, if I am

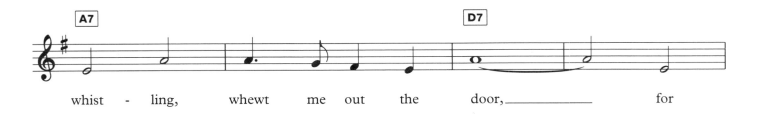

whist - ling, whewt me out the door, for

Getting To Know You

Words by Oscar Hammerstein II / Music by Richard Rodgers

Suggested Registration: Strings
Rhythm: Slow Swing
Tempo: ♩ = 104

Give My Regards To Broadway

Words and Music by George M Cohan

Suggested Registration: Piano
Rhythm: March
Tempo: ♩ = 116

Give my re-gards to Broad-way, re-mem-ber me to Her-ald

Square, tell all the gang at For - ty Sec - ond Street that

I will soon be there. Whis - per of how I'm

yearn - ing to min - gle with the old time throng,

give my re-gards to old Broad-way, and say that I'll be there e're

long. Give my re-gards to Broad-way, re-mem-ber me to Her-ald

Square, tell all the gang at For - ty Sec - ond Street that

I will soon be there. Whis - per of how I'm

yearn - ing to min - gle with the old time throng, give my re - gards to

old Broad - way, and say that I'll be there e're long.

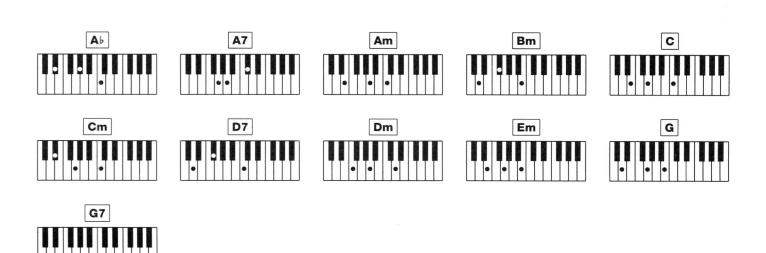

HELLO DOLLY!

Words and Music by Jerry Herman

Suggested Registration: Clarinet
Rhythm: Swing / Dixie
Tempo: ♩ = 172

Hel - lo   Dol - ly,   well   hel - lo

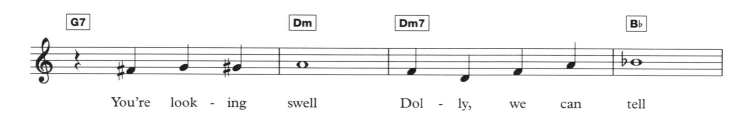

Dol - ly,   it's   so   nice   to   have   you   back   where   you   be - long.

You're   look - ing   swell   Dol - ly,   we   can   tell

Dol - ly,   you're   still   glow - in',   you're   still   crow - in',   you're   still

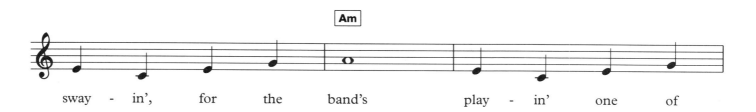

go - in'   strong.   We   feel   the   room

sway - in',   for   the   band's   play - in'   one   of

your old fav - 'rite songs from 'way back when. So

take her wrap, fel - las, find her an emp - ty lap, fel - las,

Dol - ly - 'll ne - ver go a - way, Dol - ly - 'll ne - ver go a - way,

Dol - ly - 'll ne - ver go a - way a - gain!_____

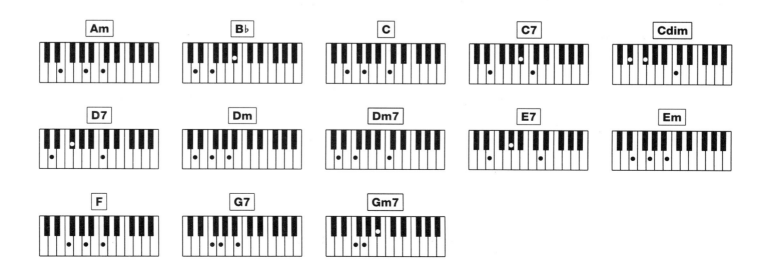

Hey There

Words and Music by Richard Adler and Jerry Ross

Suggested Registration: Strings
Rhythm: Slow Swing
Tempo: ♩ = 86

Hopelessly Devoted To You

Words and Music by John Farrar

Suggested Registration: Strings
Rhythm: Slow Rock 6/8
Tempo: ♩. = 75

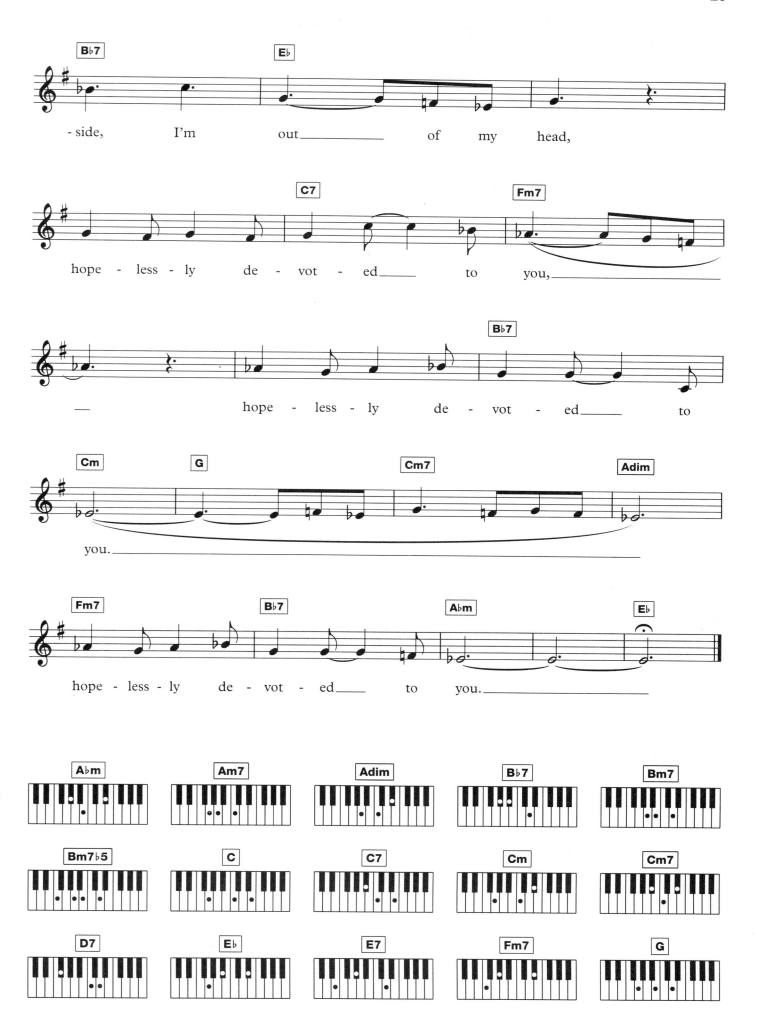

I Can't Get Started

Words by Ira Gershwin / Music by Vernon Duke

Suggested Registration: Flute
Rhythm: Slow Swing
Tempo: ♩ = 82

June Is Bustin' Out All Over

Words by Oscar Hammerstein II / Music by Richard Rodgers

Suggested Registration: Clarinet
Rhythm: March
Tempo: ♩ = 116

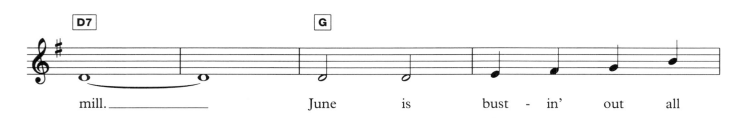

K-ra-zy For You

Music and Lyrics by George Gershwin and Ira Gershwin

Suggested Registration: Piano
Rhythm: Slow Swing
Tempo: ♩ = 98

Married

Words by Fred Ebb / Music by John Kander

Suggested Registration: Flute
Rhythm: Waltz
Tempo: ♩ = 116

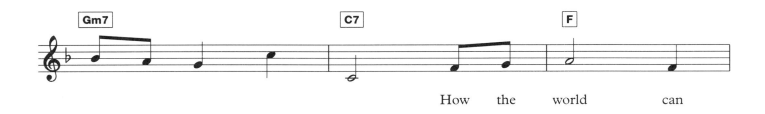

How the world can

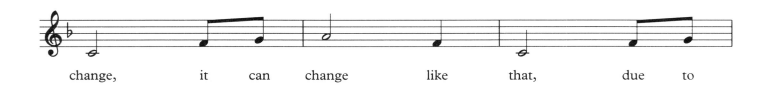

change, it can change like that, due to

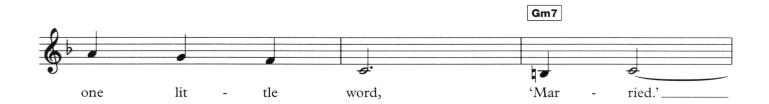

one lit - tle word, 'Mar - ried.' _____

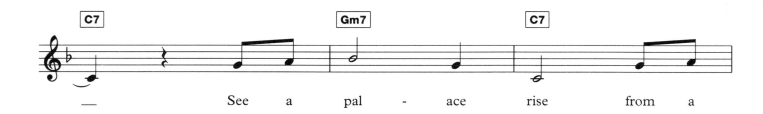

__ See a pal - ace rise from a

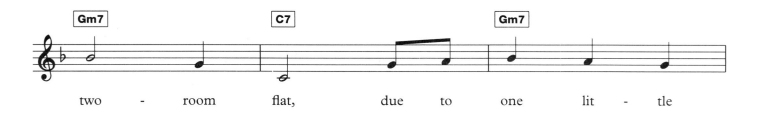

two - room flat, due to one lit - tle

Maybe

Words by Martin Charnin / Music by Charles Strouse

Suggested Registration: Harmonica
Rhythm: Soft Rock
Tempo: ♩ = 86

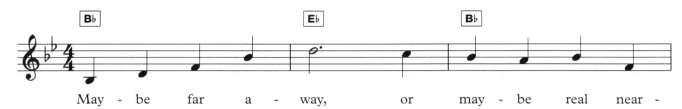

May - be far a - way, or may - be real near -

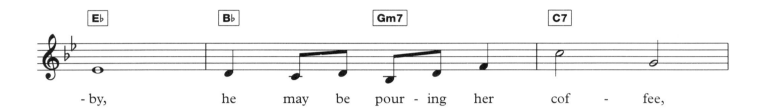

- by, he may be pour - ing her cof - fee,

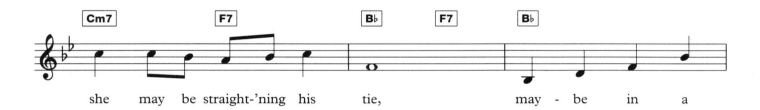

she may be straight-'ning his tie, may - be in a

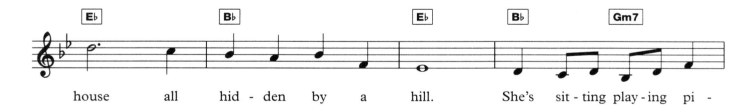

house all hid - den by a hill. She's sit - ting play - ing pi -

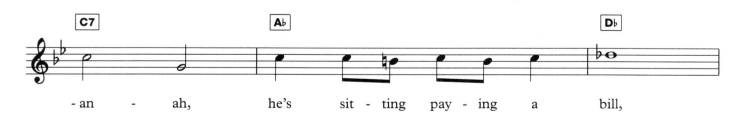

- an - ah, he's sit - ting pay - ing a bill,

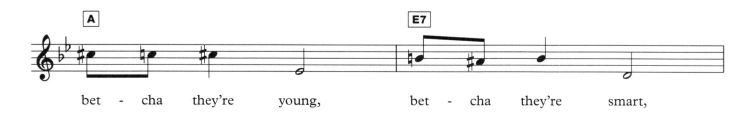

bet - cha they're young, bet - cha they're smart,

ONE

Words by Edward Lawrence Kleban / Music by Marvin Hamlisch

Suggested Registration: Clarinet
Rhythm: Swing
Tempo: ♩ = 104

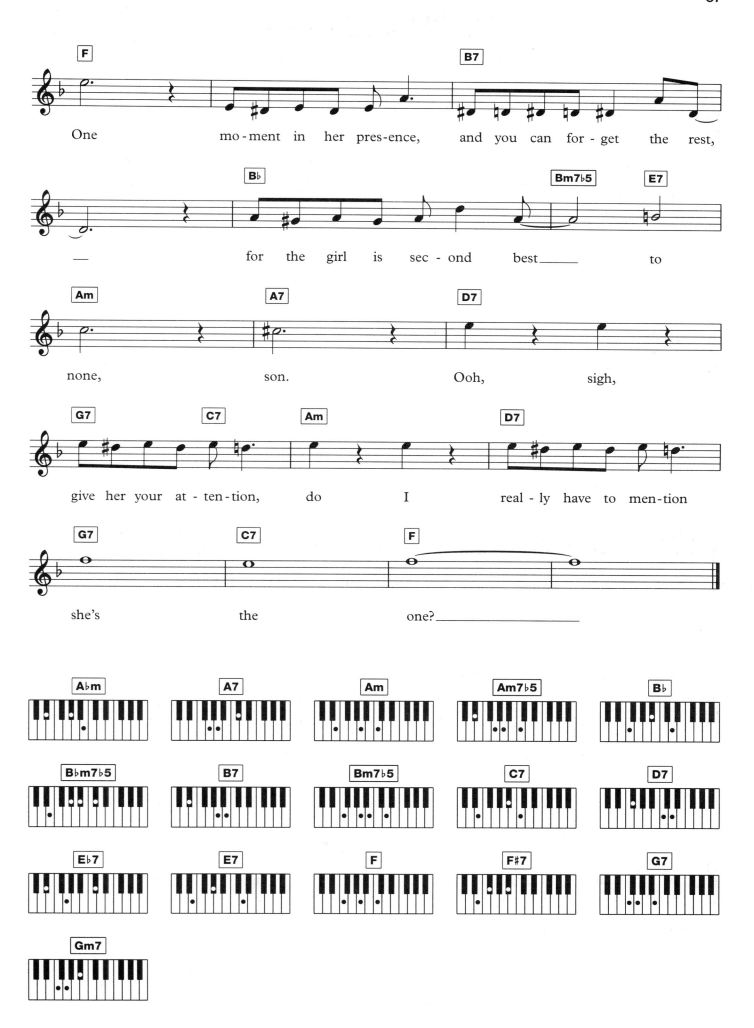

'S Wonderful

Music and Lyrics by George Gershwin and Ira Gershwin

Suggested Registration: Vibraphone
Rhythm: Swing
Tempo: ♩ = 170

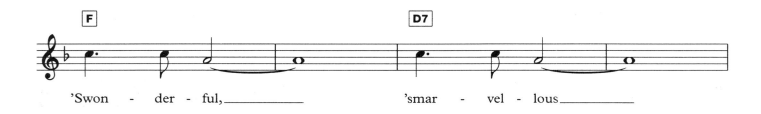

'Swon - der - ful,_____ 'smar - vel - lous_____

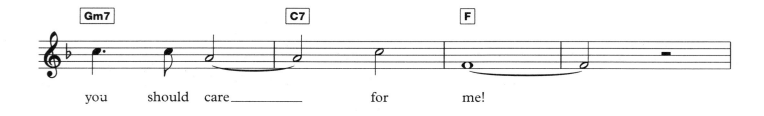

you should care_____ for me!

'Saw - ful nice,_____ 'spa - ra - dise_____

Somewhere

Words by Stephen Sondheim / Music by Leonard Bernstein

Suggested Registration: Strings
Rhythm: Soft Rock
Tempo: ♩ = 80

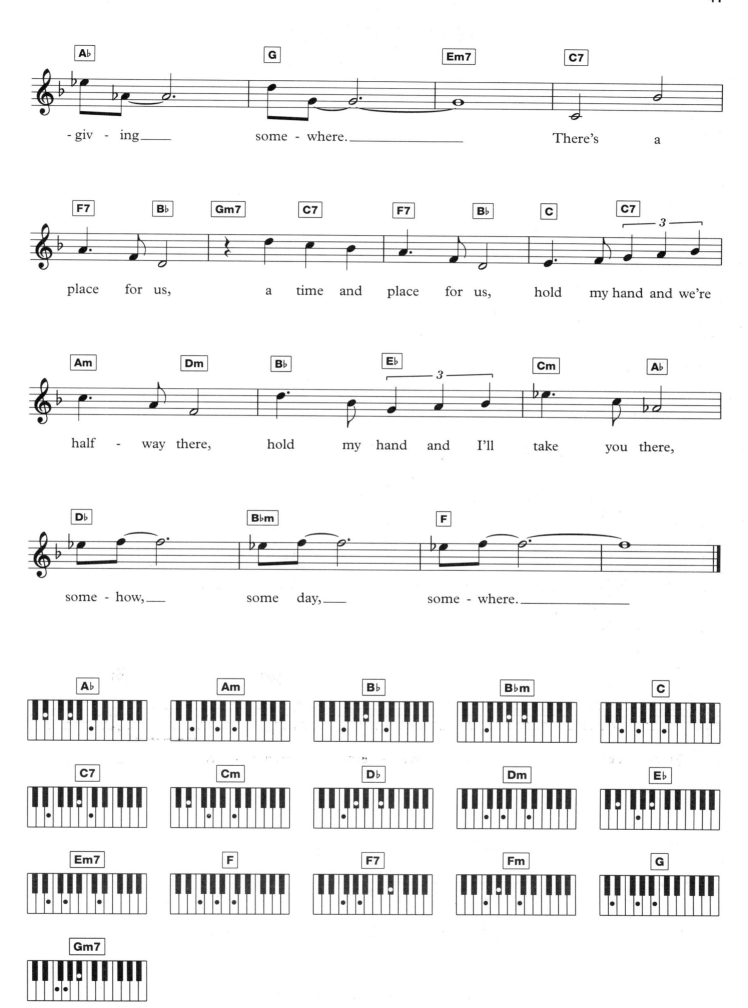

Willkommen

Words by Fred Ebb / Music by John Kander

Suggested Registration: Vibraphone
Rhythm: Swing
Tempo: ♩ = 176

Will - kom - men! Bien - ven - ue! Wel - come! _____

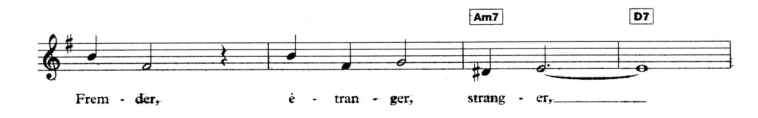

Frem - der, é - tran - ger, strang - er, _____

Glück - lich zu seh - en, je suis en - chan - té, _____

hap - py   to   see   you,   blei - be,   res - te,

stay.   Will - kom - men!   Bien - ven - ue!

Wel - come!____   Im   Ca - bar - et,_____   du   Ca - bar -

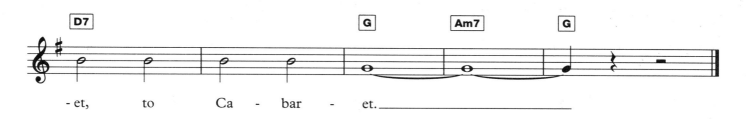

- et,   to   Ca - bar - et._____

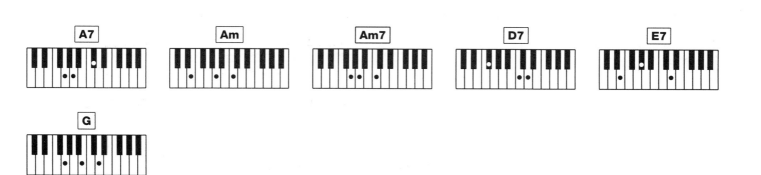

Wouldn't It Be Loverly

Words by Alan Jay Lerner / Music by Frederick Loewe

Suggested Registration: Accordian
Rhythm: Slow Swing
Tempo: ♩ = 104

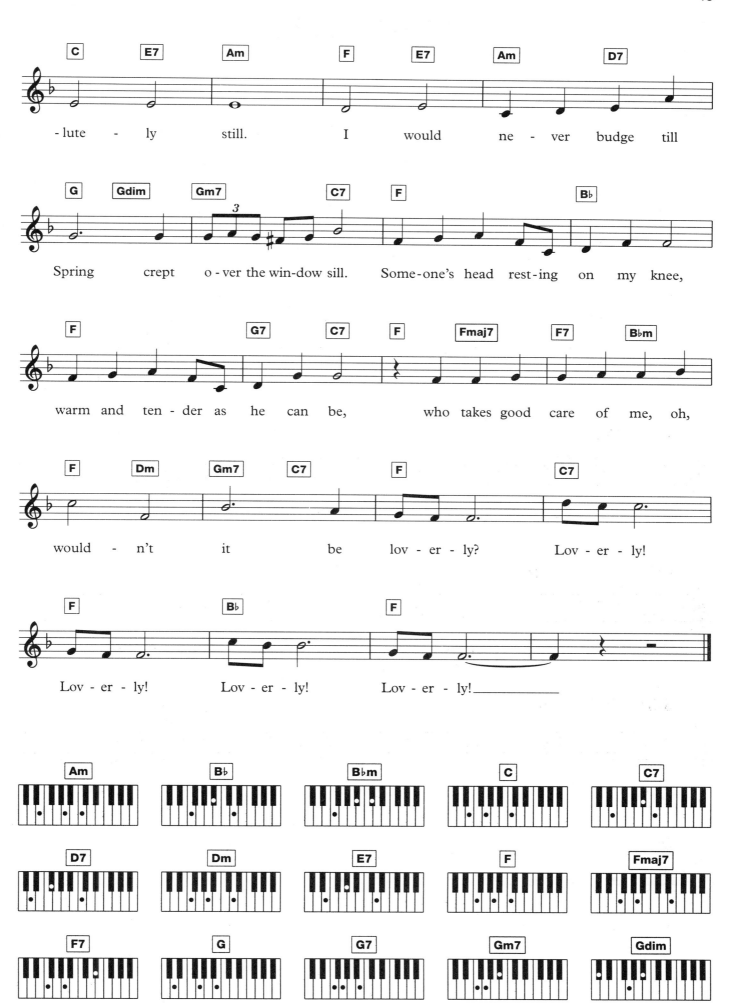

Young Girl

Words and Music by Jerry Fuller

Suggested Registration: Saxophone
Rhythm: 8 Beat
Tempo: ♩ = 132

Young girl get out of my mind,___ my love for you is

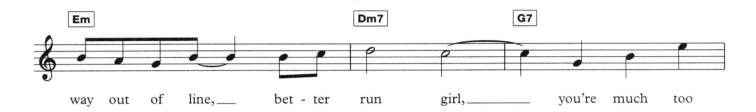

way out of line,___ bet - ter run girl,_____ you're much too

young, girl._____ With all the charms of a wo - man,

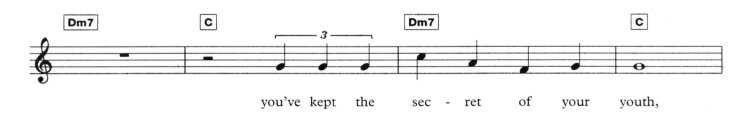

you've kept the sec - ret of your youth,

you led me to be - lieve_ you're old e - nough to

give me love,___ and now it hurts to know the

Printed by Watkiss Studios Ltd., Biggleswade, Beds. 10/95

The Easy Keyboard Library
also available in this series

Country Songs
including:
Don't It Make My Brown Eye's Blue,
Just When I Needed You Most,
The Rose and Stand By Your Man

Classic Hits Volume 1
including:
All Woman, From A Distance,
I'd Do Anything For Love
(But I Won't Do That) and Show Me Heaven

Classic Hits Volume 2
including:
Don't Go Breaking My Heart,
Heal The World,
My Baby Just Cares For Me and
What A Wonderful World

Showtunes
including:
Anything Goes, Forty-Second Street,
I Remember It Well and
Lullaby Of Broadway

Number One Hits
including:
Congratulations, Moon River,
Stand By Me and Without You

Film Classics
including:
I Will Always Love You, Chariots
Of Fire, Aces High and Mona Lisa

Love Songs Volume 1
including:
Careless Whisper,
The First Time Ever I Saw Your Face,
Saving All My Love For You
and True Love

Love Songs Volume 2
including:
I'll Be There, Love Me Tender,
Where Do I Begin? (Love Story) and
You've Lost That Lovin' Feelin'

Christmas Songs
including:
Another Rock & Roll Christmas,
Frosty The Snowman, Jingle Bells and
Mistletoe And Wine

Soul Classics
including:
Fever, My Girl, (Sittin' On) The Dock
Of The Bay and When A Man Loves
A Woman

TV Themes
including:
Birds Of A Feather, Coronation Street, Last
Of The Summer Wine and Match Of The Day

Big Band Hits
including:
Come Fly With Me, In The Mood,
It's Only A Paper Moon and Secret Love

THE EASY KEYBOARD LIBRAR